HELLO KITTY®

Coloring and Activity Book

Hello Kitty®

Let's pick some flowers!

Finish the Picture

Connect the dots and then color the picture.

1 ★
2
3
4
5
6
9
8 7 17
18 19 20
21
22
16
10
15
23
11
12 13 14
24 25
32
31
30
29
28
27
26

Answers in the back.

Which Picture is Different?

1.

2.

3.

4.

Answers in the back.

Can you figure out which route Hello Kitty flew in her airplane?

Route 1

Route 2

Route 3

Route 4

Answers in the back.

Finish the Picture

Finish drawing the boat.

HOW MANY?

Count the items below and place your answer on the line.

_____ BOATS.

WHICH IS WHICH?

Draw a line from each shadow to the
character to which it belongs.

Answers in the back.

Fire Station No. 9

Hello Kitty visits the fire station.

Fight the Fire!

Help Hello Kitty and her fire fighting friends put out the fire. Find the way from the fire hydrant to the flames.

Answers in the back.

Grandpa

Grandma

HELLO KITTY® SQUARES

Taking turns, connect a line from one star to another. Whoever makes the line that completes a box puts their initials inside the box. The person with the most squares at the end of the game wins!

EXAMPLE:

My Friends

Rorry   Joey

Tim Tammy   Tracy   Thomas

Tippy

Fifi

Jodie

You are Hello Kitty's friend too. Draw a picture of yourself.

NAME: _____

Mimmy

My Family

Mama

Papa

HOW MANY?

Count the items below and place your answer on the line.

_____ APPLES.

Which Picture is Different?

1.

2.

3.

4.

Answers in the back.

HOW MANY?
Count the items below and
place your answer on the line.

_____ COWS.

Home Sweet Home!

HELLO KITTY® SQUARES

Taking turns, connect a line from one flower to another. Whoever makes the line that completes a box puts their initials inside the box. The person with the most squares at the end of the game wins!

EXAMPLE:

Hello Kitty loves to go ice skating!

HELLO KITTY®

HOW MANY?

Count the items below and
place your answer on the line.

_____ MITTENS.

HOW MANY?
Count the items below and place your answer on the line.

_____ COOKIES.

Market

After school, Hello Kitty rides her bicycle to the market.

Twin Policemen!

Can you spot the twins?
Which two policemen are
exactly the same?

Answers in the back.

HOW MANY?
Count the items below and
place your answer on the line.

_____ MUSHROOMS.

©1976, 2011 SANRIO CO., LTD.

TREASURE HUNT

Hello kitty needs to find all of the items on the list below to put into the box. Can you find and circle all 8 items?

FIND SOMETHING TO EAT.   FIND SOMETHING WITH PETALS.

FIND SOMETHING THAT FLIES.   FIND SOMETHING THAT FLOATS.

FIND A CIRCLE.   FIND A STAR.

FIND A HEXAGON.   FIND SOMETHING TO WEAR.

Answers in Back

Connect the dots to see who has a special delivery!

MAIL

Answers in the back.

HOW MANY?
Count the items below and place your answer on the line.

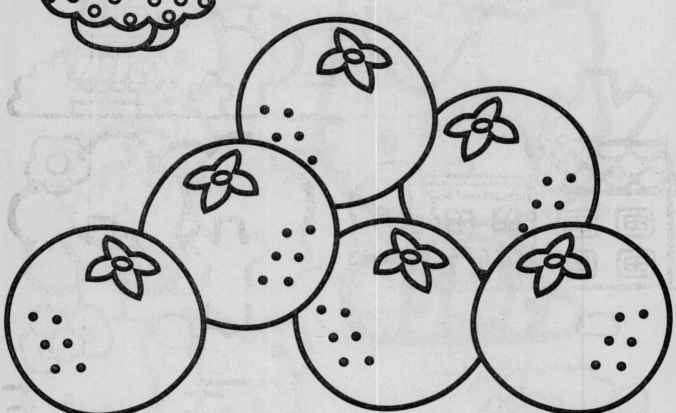

_____ ORANGES.

Flower Find!

Can you find the 11 flowers that are hidden
in the picture? Circle the flowers as you find them.

Answers in the back.

Best Friends!

Finish the Picture
Finish drawing the heart.

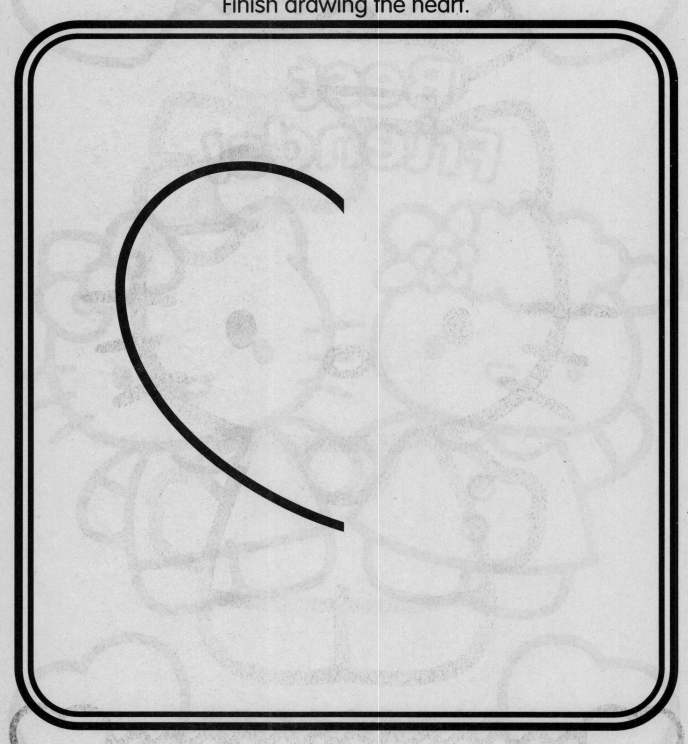

HOW MANY?

Count the items below and
place your answer on the line.

_____ ANCHORS.

Answer: 7 ANCHORS.

HELLO KITTY®

Lunch Time!

Which Picture is Different?

1.

2.

3.

4.

Answers in the back.

WHICH IS WHICH?

Draw a line from each shadow to the character to which it belongs.

Answers in the back.

Help the bus driver find his way to the school!

Answer in the back.

Can you find the crayon set that matches?

Color by Letter

Using the key below as a guide, finish
the picture of Hello Kitty.

A=Green   B=Blue   C=Yellow   D=White
E=Orange   F=Red   G=Brown

Finish the Picture

Finish drawing Hello Kitty.

How many words can you make by using the letters in

FLOWER BOUQUET

Which Picture is Different?

1.

2.

3.

4.

Answers in the back.

Look at all the pretty flowers Hello Kitty planted!

Connect the dots to see what Hello Kitty is doing on the farm!

Answers in the back.

Howdy!

HOW MANY?
Count the items below and place your answer on the line.

BABY CHICKS.

_____

Flower Power
Can you match the flowers to the right pots?

Which Picture is Different?

WHICH IS WHICH?
Draw a line from each shadow to the
picture that matches it below.

1.

2.

3.

4.

Answers in the back.

WHICH IS WHICH?

Draw a line from each shadow to the
character to which it belongs.

Answers in the back.

HELLO KITTY® SQUARES

Taking turns, connect a line from one apple to another. Whoever makes the line that completes a box puts their initials inside the box. The person with the most squares at the end of the game wins!

EXAMPLE:

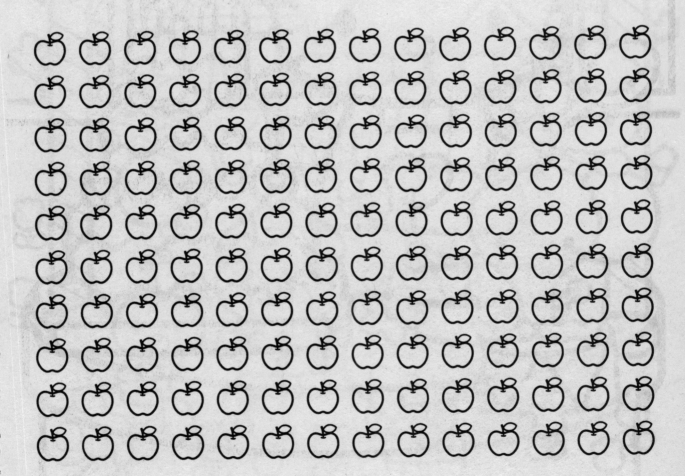

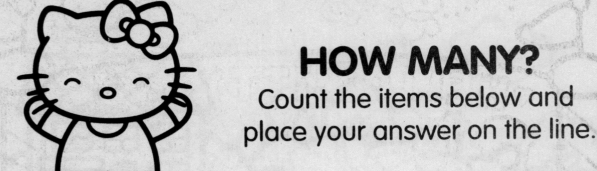

HOW MANY?

Count the items below and
place your answer on the line.

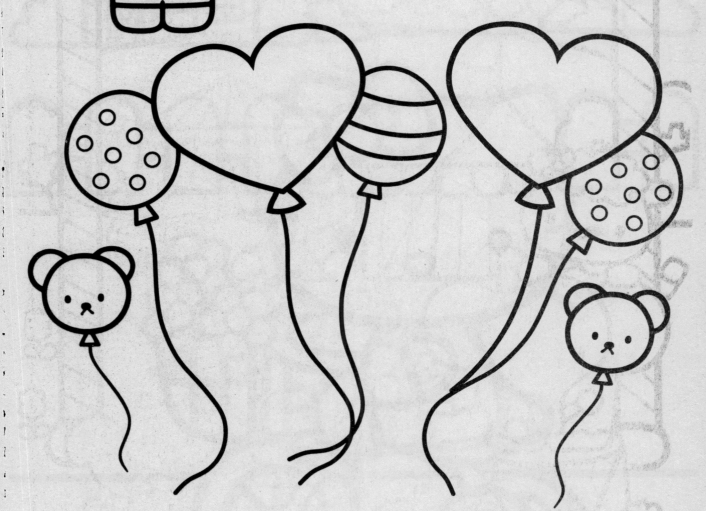

BALLOONS.

_____

What does Hello Kitty need for this sport?

Connect the dots to see!

tennis

21
22
20
1
19
2
18
3
17
4
16
7
5
15
8
6
14
9
10
13
12
11

Answers in the back.

HELLO KiTTY®

©1976, 2011 SANRIO CO., LTD.

HOW MANY?
Count the items below and place your answer on the line.

_____ NOTES.

Find the Match
Draw a line from each character
to his or her name.

Jodie

Tracy

Fifi

Tippy

Answers in the back.

Aloha!

Surf's Up!
Can you help Hello Kitty find her way back to the beach?

End

Start

Answer in the back.

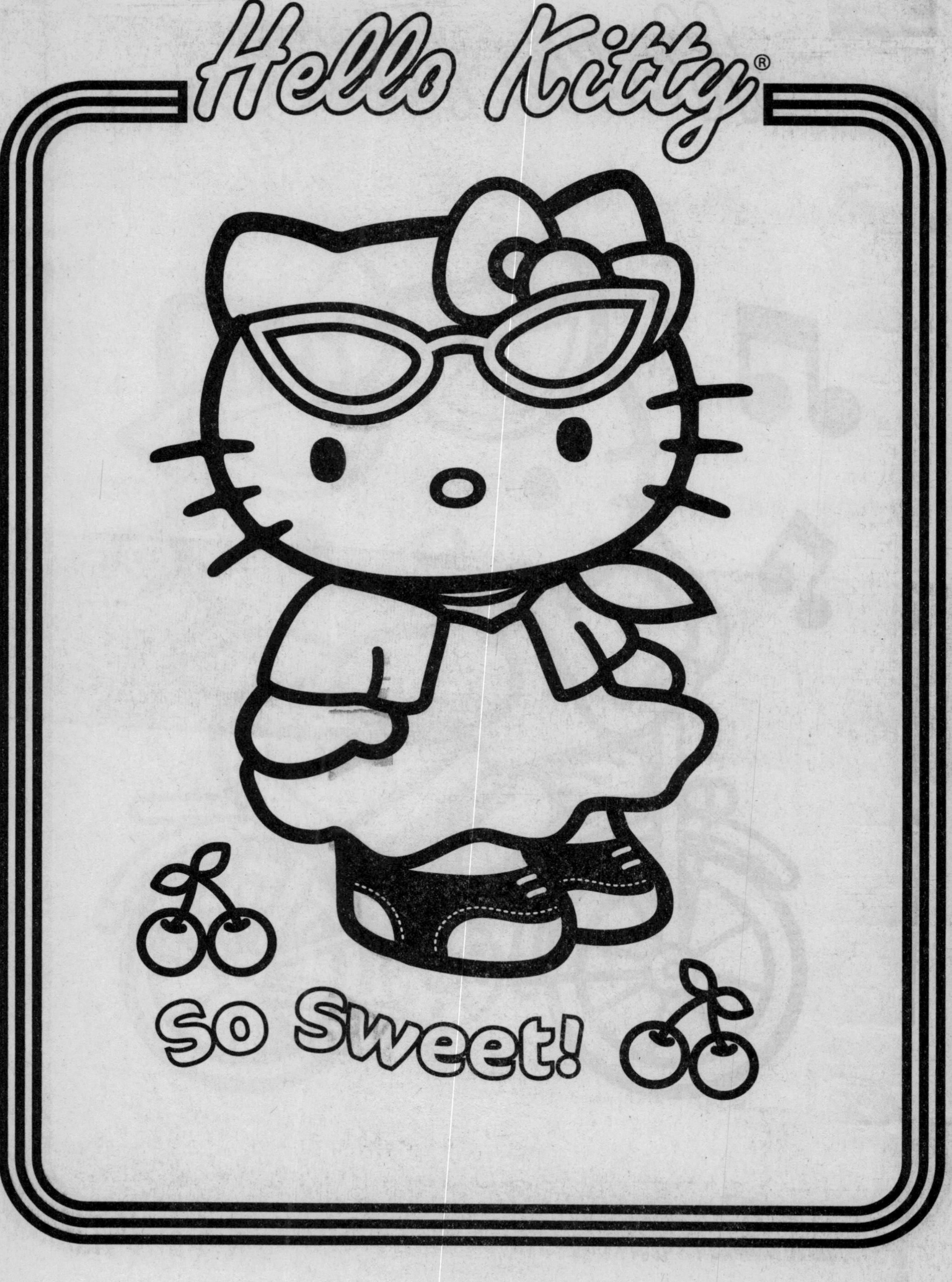
Hello Kitty®
So Sweet!

Hello Kitty

Tic-Tac-Toe Fun!

Hello Kitty®

ROCK-N-RoII!

HELLO KiTTY®

HOW MANY?

Count the items below and
place your answer on the line.

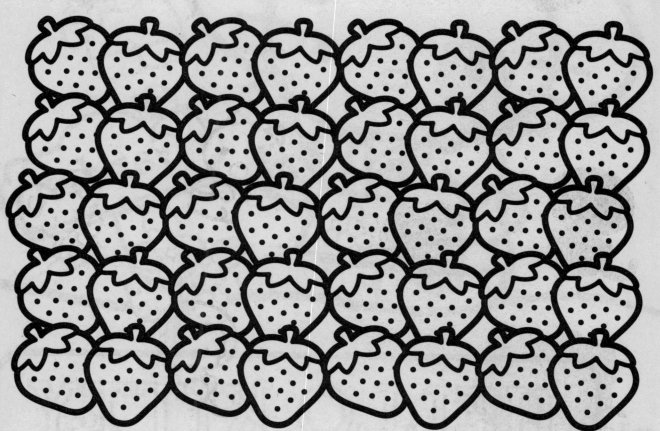

_____ STRAWBERRIES.

WHICH IS WHICH?

Draw a line from each shadow to the
character to which it belongs.

Answers in the back.

How many words can you make by using the letters in

BUTTERFLY GARDEN

_____   _____

_____   _____

_____   _____

_____   _____

_____   _____

_____   _____

HOW MANY?

Count the items below and place your answer on the line.

_____ BUTTERFLIES.

Which Picture is Different?

1.

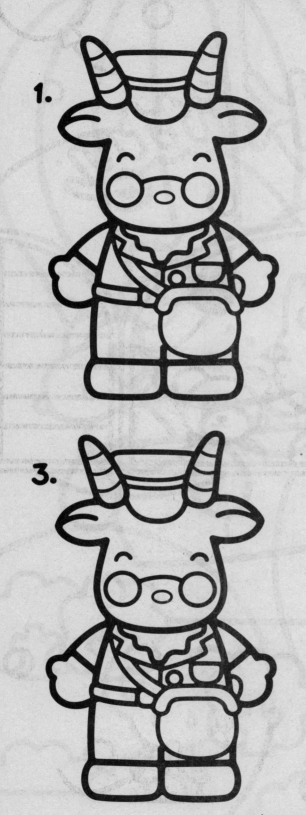

2.

3.

4.

Answers in the back.

Grandpa

Grandma

Finish the Picture

Finish drawing Mama.

Garden

HOW MANY?
Count the items below and place your answer on the line.

_____ TOMATOES.

Hello Kitty's friends like to visit the library to read books.

Reading is fun!

Draw a portrait
of your best friend!

Hello Kitty®

Tic-Tac-Toe Fun!

How Many Butterflies?

Help Hello Kitty find the butterflies.
Circle and count the butterflies.

Answers in the back.

Find the Pair

Hello Kitty would like to buy some shoes...but they are all mixed up! Help her find the ONE pair of matching shoes by drawing a line from one shoe to the other. Look carefully! The shoes have to be an EXACT match.

Answers in the back.

WHICH IS WHICH?

Draw a line from each shadow to the
character to which it belongs.

Answers in the back.

Hello Kitty is looking for her other shoe.
Find and circle the shoe that matches.

Answers in the back.

My Friends

Jodie   Tippy

Rorry

Joey

Tracy   Thomas

Tim & Tammy

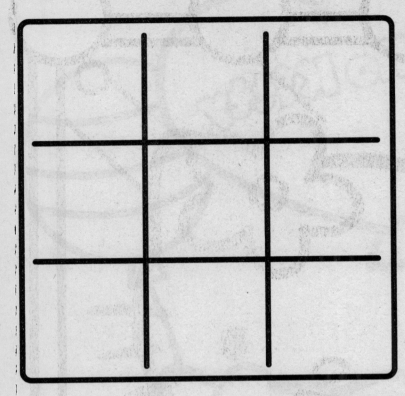

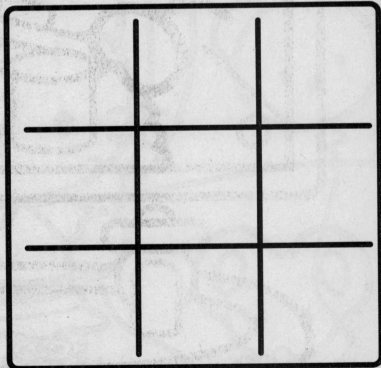

Tic-Tac-Toe Fun!

HOW MANY?
Count the items below and place your answer on the line.

_____ **HEARTS.**

Draw Hello Kitty in a space suit.

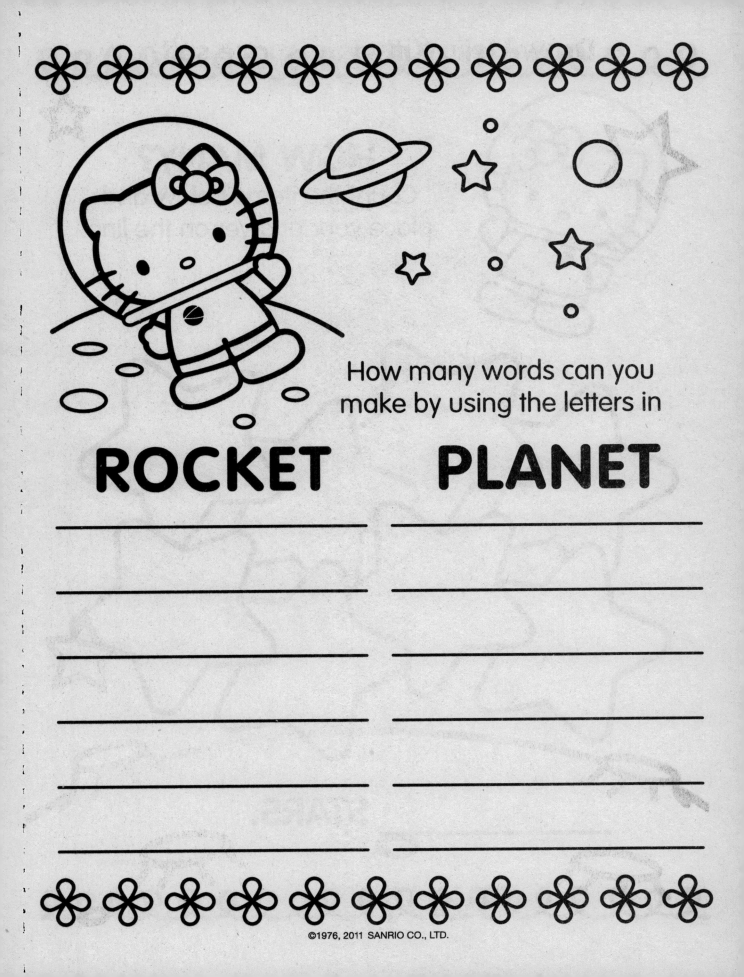

How many words can you make by using the letters in

ROCKET

PLANET

_____

_____

_____

_____

_____

_____

_____

_____

_____

_____

_____

_____

HOW MANY?
Count the items below and
place your answer on the line.

_____ STARS.

HELLO KITTY® SQUARES

Taking turns, connect a line from one flower to another. Whoever makes the line that completes a box puts their initials inside the box. The person with the most squares at the end of the game wins!

EXAMPLE:

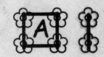

Find the Match
Draw a line from each character
to his or her name.

Thomas

Mimmy   **Jodie**

Answers in the back.

HELLO KITTY® SQUARES

Taking turns, connect a line from one heart to another. Whoever makes the line that completes a box puts their initials inside the box. The person with the most squares at the end of the game wins!

EXAMPLE:

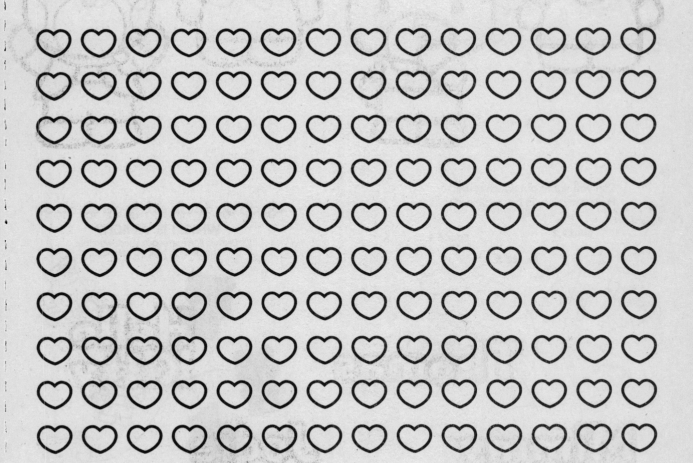

Answers

❀❀❀❀❀❀❀❀❀❀❀
Finish the Picture
Connect the dots and then color the picture.

Answers in the back.

❀❀❀❀❀❀❀❀❀❀❀

Which Picture is Different?

Answers in the back.

Can you figure out which route Hello Kitty flew in her airplane?

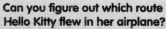

Answers in the back.

❀❀❀❀❀❀❀❀❀❀❀
WHICH IS WHICH?
Draw a line from each shadow to the character to which it belongs.

Answers in the back.

❀❀❀❀❀❀❀❀❀❀❀

✿ Answers ✿

Fight the Fire!
Help Hello Kitty and her fire fighting friends put out the fire. Find the way from the fire hydrant to the flames.

Which Picture is Different?

Answers in the back.

Twin Policemen!
Can you spot the twins? Which two policemen are exactly the same?

TREASURE HUNT
Hello kitty needs to find all of the items on the list below to put into the box. Can you find and circle all 8 items?

FIND SOMETHING TO EAT.   FIND SOMETHING WITH PETALS.
FIND SOMETHING THAT FLIES.   FIND SOMETHING THAT FLOATS.
FIND A CIRCLE.   FIND A STAR.
FIND A HEXAGON.   FIND SOMETHING TO WEAR.

❀ Answers ❀

❀❀❀❀❀❀❀❀❀

Connect the dots to see who has a special delivery!

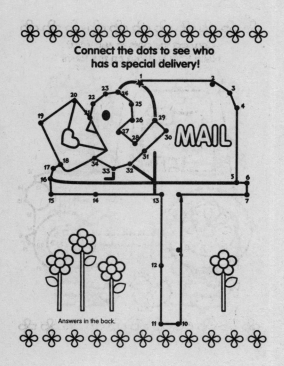

MAIL

Answers in the back.

❀❀❀❀❀❀❀❀❀

Flower Find!
Can you find the 11 flowers that are hidden in the picture? Circle the flowers as you find them.

Which Picture is Different?

1.
2.
3.
4.

Answers in the back.

❀❀❀❀❀❀❀❀❀

WHICH IS WHICH?
Draw a line from each shadow to the character to which it belongs.

❀❀❀❀❀❀❀❀❀

❀ Answers ❀

Help the bus driver find his way to the school!

Connect the dots to see what
Hello Kitty is doing on the farm!

Which Picture is Different?

1.

2.

3.

4.

Answers in the back.

WHICH IS WHICH?

Draw a line from each shadow to the
character to which it belongs.

Answers in the back.

✿ Answers ✿

What does Hello Kitty need for this sport?
Connect the dots to see!

Answers in the back.

Find the Match
Draw a line from each character to his or her name.

Jodie

Tracy

Fifi

Tippy

Surf's Up!
Can you help Hello Kitty find her way back to the beach?

End

Start

WHICH IS WHICH?
Draw a line from each shadow to the character to which it belongs.

Answers in the back.

🌸 Answers 🌸

Which Picture is Different?

Answers in the back.

How Many Butterflies?

Help Hello Kitty find the butterflies. Circle and count the butterflies.

Answers in the back.

Find the Pair

Hello Kitty would like to buy some shoes...but they are all mixed up! Help her find the ONE pair of matching shoes by drawing a line from one shoe to the other. Look carefully! The shoes have to be an EXACT match.

WHICH IS WHICH?

Draw a line from each shadow to the character to which it belongs.

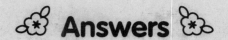

Answers

Hello Kitty is looking for her other shoe.
Find and circle the shoe that matches.

✿✿✿✿✿✿✿✿✿

Find the Match

Draw a line from each character
to his or her name.

Thomas

Hello Kitty

Mimmy

Jodie

Answers in the back.

✿✿✿✿✿✿✿✿✿